Contents

Ben rides his bike
Focus on: i_e as in *like*.................................. 3

Cats at night
Focus on: igh as in *night* 8

Lots of pies!
Focus on: ie, y as in *tie,* fl*y*.......................... 17

Phonemes: ch, sh, th, wh, ph, a_e, ai, ay, e_e, ea, ee, y *as e*, **i_e, ie, igh, y** *as i*
'Tricky' words: my, can't, does, love, here, are, look, our, eyes

About this book

These short stories are designed to give children blending and reading practice. They are decodable, which means the words in them only include letter shapes and sounds that the children have learned. The stories gradually introduce 'tricky' words, building on the learning in the Red Series.

The progression links directly to the teaching order in the Letterland teaching range. Each story begins with a title page that provides important information for children and teachers.

Story title

Focus on: New spelling patterns introduced

New 'tricky' words: Common words with irregular spellings

Basic teaching tips:

- Encourage the sounding out of decodable words (and any decodable parts of 'tricky' words).
- Discuss the stories with the children to ensure comprehension and engagement.
- Encourage re-reading in pairs or individually to develop fluency and reading for meaning.

Red Series introduces the a-z letters and sounds and some 'tricky words'. On completion of this series, the following words remain tricky in part: **a, the, she, oh, for, that, ok, they, says, her, this, to, said, of, what, you, was, want, come, sees, asks, do.** These words are included in **Blue Series**.

Ben rides his bike

Focus on: i_e as in *like*

It is a fine day. Ben rides his bike in the sunshine. He waves at Red Robot as he rakes up a big pile by a pine tree.

Nick is by the compost bin. Ben waves to Nick. He waves back as he bangs the lid nine times.

Next, Ben rides by Mike on the slide.

Ben smiles and waves as Mike begins to slide.

He makes a big splash!

Mike gets quite wet, but Ben is fine.

Cats at night

Tricky words: look, our, eyes

Teaching Tip
This story can be read as a play. Cast members include: Miss High, Mike, Kate Meg, Zack.

Focus on: igh as in *ni__gh__t*

Miss High: Let's study our eyes.

Mike: My cat has bright green eyes.

Miss High: Yes, but we are going to study <u>our</u> eyes.

Kate: Cats can see at night.

Zack: My cat got in a fight last night. It gave me a fright!

Meg: My cat's eyes are bright if you shine a light in them.

Miss High: Okay, okay, we <u>might</u> study cats' eyes for a bit!
In the daylight we can see just as well as cats. At night, our eyes open up, but cats' eyes open up a lot!

Kate: I am right!

Miss High: If there is a slight bit of light, like starlight, cats can see at night. But cats can't see when there is no light.

Mike: So, do our eyes open up like this?

Miss High: Not quite like that, Mike. Look at a classmate's eyes. Look at the black dot in the eye.

Zack: Yes, I can see the black dots, Mike!

Miss High: Meg, please switch off the light and shut the blind.

Miss High: It is not as bright. Look at the black dots again.

Zack: Jake. Look! They <u>are</u> big!

Miss High: Yes, they open to let in the light.

Kate: I must be a cat. I can see!

Miss High: There is still a bit of light.

Meg: Can I bring my cat to class?

Miss High: No, but we can study cats' eyes reflecting light.

Class: Yes! Lots of cat study, please! We like cats!

Lots of pies!

Focus on: ie, y
as in *tie*, *fly*

The pup tried to make a pie.
He put in paint, that's not a lie!

I don't want to try the pup's paint pie.

The cat tried to make a pie.
It was crispy, she began to cry.

I don't want to try the cat's crisp pie.

Then Fred tried to make a pie.
But he did not see the five fat flies.

I don't want to try Fred's fly pie.

Dippy tried to make a pie.
With just duckweed it was quite dry.

I don't want to try dry duckweed pie.

These fine men can make nice pies.
"Make nine!" "Make ten!" the pals cried.

Which pie do you want to try?

About this series

This series of 10 books accompanies the Letterland teaching range. Each book contains a selection of short stories. In total there are 32 engaging stories featuring the phonic elements listed below as well as some 'tricky' high-frequency words.

Book	Focus elements	As in the word...	Story titles
1	sh, ch, th, th, wh, ph	chip, shop, that, thing	Check on the chicks Shep and me What is that thing?
2	a_e, ai, ay	make, rain, say,	A safe place Kate bakes a cake Kane's tail!
3	e_e, ea, ee, y	these, sea, bee, baby	A trip to the sea Mr E's trees Happy!
4	i_e, ie, igh, y	like, tie, night, my	Ben rides his bike Cats at night What a mess!
5	o_e, oa, ow	home, boat, show	The bad goat When the cold wind blows Lost in the Queen's maze
6	u_e, ue, oo, ew	cube, blue, moon, few, grew	Stuck on a dune A day at the zoo The Hat Man's new roof
7	ar, or, er, ir, ur, wr	farm, for, her, girl, fur, write	The big match Snapshots The bird girls My very bad morning
8	o, oo, u, oy, oi	son, book, put, boy, coin	Oscar's brother The big pull Nick's noisy new toy
9	aw, au, ow, ou	saw, cause, how, out,	Draw it! The house mouse Look now!
10	Review ear, air	pear, year, fair	My shark dream A fresh feast Bears at the fair A fairy story

23

Collect the sets

Phonics Readers - Red Series

Phonics Readers - Blue Series

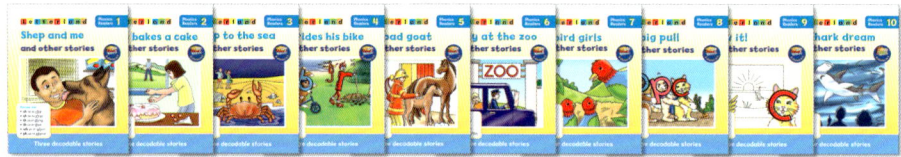

Published by Letterland International Ltd. 8/10 South Street, Epsom, Surrey, KT18 7PF, UK.
www.letterland.com
ISBN: 978-1-78248-183-6
Product Code: TJ05

© Letterland International 2016
LETTERLAND™ is a trademark of Letterland International Ltd.

First published 2013. This new edition published 2016.
Reprinted 2023.
10 9 8 7 6 5 4 3 2

Authors: Stamey Carter and Lisa Holt
Originator of Letterland: Lyn Wendon
Artwork: Doreen Shaw
Design: Lisa Holt

The author asserts the moral right to be identified as the author of this work. All rights reserved. No part of this publication may be reproduced, stored in a retrieval system, or transmitted in any form or by any means, electronic, mechanical, photocopying, recording or otherwise, without either the prior permission of the Publisher or a licence permitting restricted copying in the United Kingdom issued by the Copyright Licensing Agency Ltd, 90 Tottenham Court Road, London W1T 4LP. This book is sold subject to the condition that it shall not be way of trade or otherwise be lent, hired out or otherwise circulated without the Publisher's prior consent.

Printed in Beirut, Lebanon.